Acting

by Cathy West

Ransom

StarStruck

Acting

by Cathy West

Illustrated by Jan Martin

Published by Ransom Publishing Ltd.
Radley House, 8 St. Cross Road, Winchester, Hants. SO23 9HX
www.ransom.co.uk

ISBN   978 184167 482 7

First published in 2011

A CIP catalogue record of this book is available from the British Library.

The rights of Anita Loughrey and of Stephen Rickard to be identified as the authors and of Jan Martin to be identified as the illustrator of this Work have been asserted by them in accordance with sections 77 and 78 of the Copyright, Design and Patents Act 1988.

Acting

Contents

All About Acting

The exciting part of acting ...
I don't know how else to explain it,
are those moments when you
surprise yourself.

Tom Cruise, actor

What is acting?

An actor usually plays a character in a play or a film.

The actor pretends to be that person.

The actor usually follows a script. This tells the actor what to say and what to do.

Many famous actors started acting at school.

Actors work with other actors and with the director of the film or the play.

The director helps the actor get the best performance.

Famous actors

How many of these actors do you know?

The answers are on page 18.

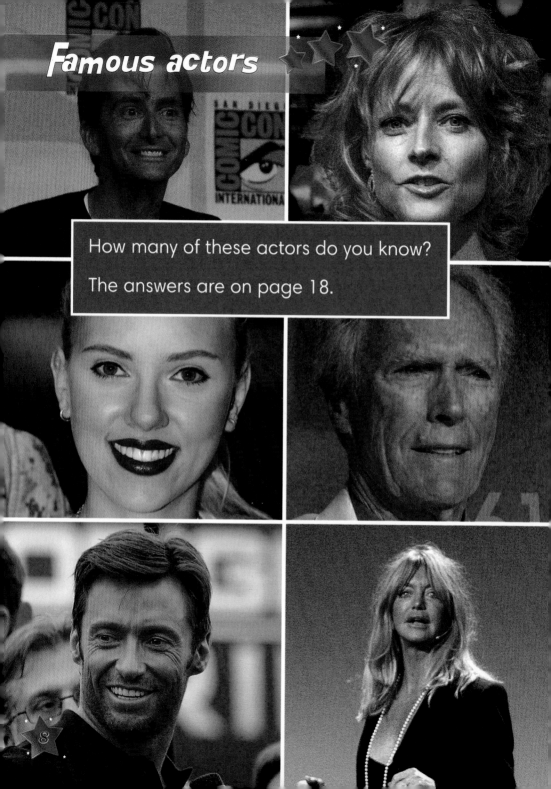

Acting in the theatre

In the theatre, the actors perform on the stage. The audience watches the performance.

Acting in the theatre is very different from acting in a film or on TV.

A masked actor in a play in China.

In the theatre:

- The actors cannot stop and start again if they make a mistake.

- Everything is 'live': the audience watches the actors as they perform the play.

- The actors must remember all of their lines (the words the actors speak) for the whole play.

- The actors perform the play every night. There is a different audience each time.

- The whole play happens on the stage. The actors use scenery, stage lighting and stage makeup to make the play more realistic.

STAGE DOOR

11

Acting in film and television

Acting for film or television is not like acting in the theatre.

In film and television:

The actors perform in a short scene.

Later, they act in a different scene.

Actors often film their scenes in the wrong order.

If the actors make a mistake, they can start again.

Each scene is filmed.

At the end, all the short scenes, or takes, are cut together, or edited.

This makes the final movie.

An actor can work on a movie for many months.

But sometimes it takes another year to finish the movie.

Method acting

Some actors try to become the character they play.

- They try to think like the character.

- They try to speak and move like the character.

- Instead of acting the part, they try being the part.

This is called method acting.

Some actors just call it 'the method'.

Sometimes method actors carry on playing the part even when they are not acting.

They stay 'in character'.

- At home they think like the character.

- They eat in character.

- They even talk to their friends in character.

These actors have used 'the method':

Dustin Hoffman
James Dean
Robert De Niro

15

A career in acting

What you need

- You need talent.
- You need to be determined.
- You need to work hard.
- You need luck, too!

It's not easy. Lots of people want to be actors. Most don't make it.

Starting out

There are many ways to become an actor.

It helps if you go to drama school. But the most important thing is to get lots of experience.

Try to work with local theatre groups. Or try acting at school or college.

Auditions

An audition is a bit like a job interview. The actor gives a short performance.

It shows if the actor would be good for the part.

Getting work

Most actors have an agent to help them get work. The actors pay the agent to get work for them.

Actors need to audition for each part they try to get.

Most actors go a long time with no work. So it's good to have a second job.

! Harrison Ford was a carpenter until he could make acting pay.

17

Famous actors

The actors on pages 8 and 9 are:

David Tennant
Jodie Foster
Jessica Alba
Patrick Stewart

Scarlett Johansson
Clint Eastwood
George Clooney
Miley Cyrus

Hugh Jackman
Goldie Hawn
Helen Mirren
Leonardo DiCaprio

Stella Dreams of Stardom

Chapter One

Big dreams

Stella worked in the theatre. She sold theatre programmmes.

During the show, she always stood at the back and watched the actors on the stage. Stella wished she could be like them.

Stella knew all the actors' lines. She often said the lines aloud at the same time as the actors on the stage.

She thought no one was listening. But she was wrong!

Stella loved acting.

Romeo, Romeo, wherefore art thou Romeo?

She knew all the actors' lines.

'Shhh!'

Her friend Hannah nudged her.

'That man's watching you.' Hannah pointed to a man sat in the back row.

Stella blushed. 'Who is he? He keeps staring at me. I hope he doesn't complain to the boss.'

For the rest of the show, Stella was worried. If the man complained, she could lose her job.

Chapter Two

Lucky break

At the end of the show, the man walked over to Stella. She tried to run and hide. But there were too many people to get past.

She had no choice. She had to talk to him.

'I'm sorry if I disturbed the show,' she said. 'You must think I'm crazy!'

'I thought you were very good,' the man said. 'Have you ever thought about a career in acting?'

'It's all I ever dream about,' Stella told him.

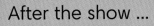

'My name is Paul. I work at a television studio,' he said. 'We're filming tomorrow. I think you are the person we've been looking for.'

He gave Stella his card. Stella stood with her mouth open.

'Be at the studio – nine o'clock tomorrow morning,' Paul said.

'Thank you, Paul,' she mumbled.

She ran to tell Hannah.

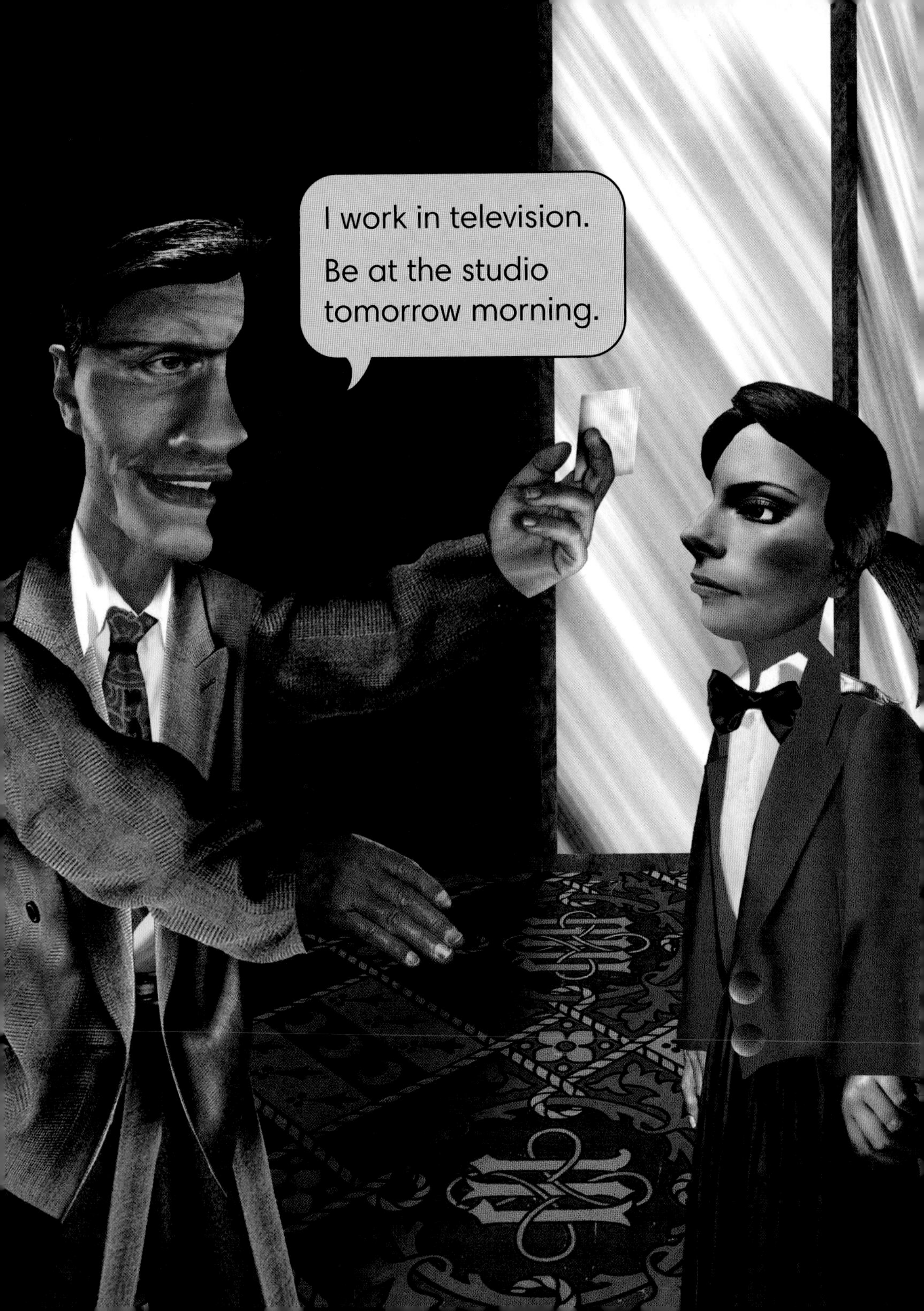
I work in television.
Be at the studio tomorrow morning.

Chapter Three

It must be a joke

'I'm going to be on TV!'

Stella showed Hannah Paul's business card.

'It's too good to be true,' Hannah said. 'It must be a joke!'

'You're just jealous.'

'Just be careful,' Hannah warned her friend. 'You don't know anything about this man.'

I'm going to be on TV!
Just be careful. You don't know anything about him.

Stella arrived at the television studio on time. She went to the front desk to sign in. A woman checked the list of names.

'Yes, here you are.' The woman pointed to Stella's name on the list. 'Paul's waiting for you upstairs.'

She gave Stella a name badge and handed her a jar of coffee.

'Third floor. And take this with you. You're going to need it!'

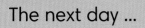

Chapter Four

Can dreams come true?

Stella's heart sank. Hannah was right. It **was** too good to be true. All he wanted was someone to make the coffee.

The lift reached the third floor. Paul was waiting there for Stella.

'Great!' he said. 'You brought the coffee.'

He took her into the TV studio. There were cameras and lots of people with lights and microphones. It was very different to the theatre.

'I'll put the kettle on, right away,' said Stella.

'You're not here to make coffee!' Paul said. 'We're making an advert for a new brand of coffee. We want you to be the star.'

Stella looked at the jar in her hand. It was called Romeo Coffee.

'Say the line I heard you say at the theatre, yesterday.'

Stella grinned. She held the jar of coffee up to the camera.

'Romeo, Romeo, wherefore art thou Romeo?'

It looked like it **was** a lucky break, after all!

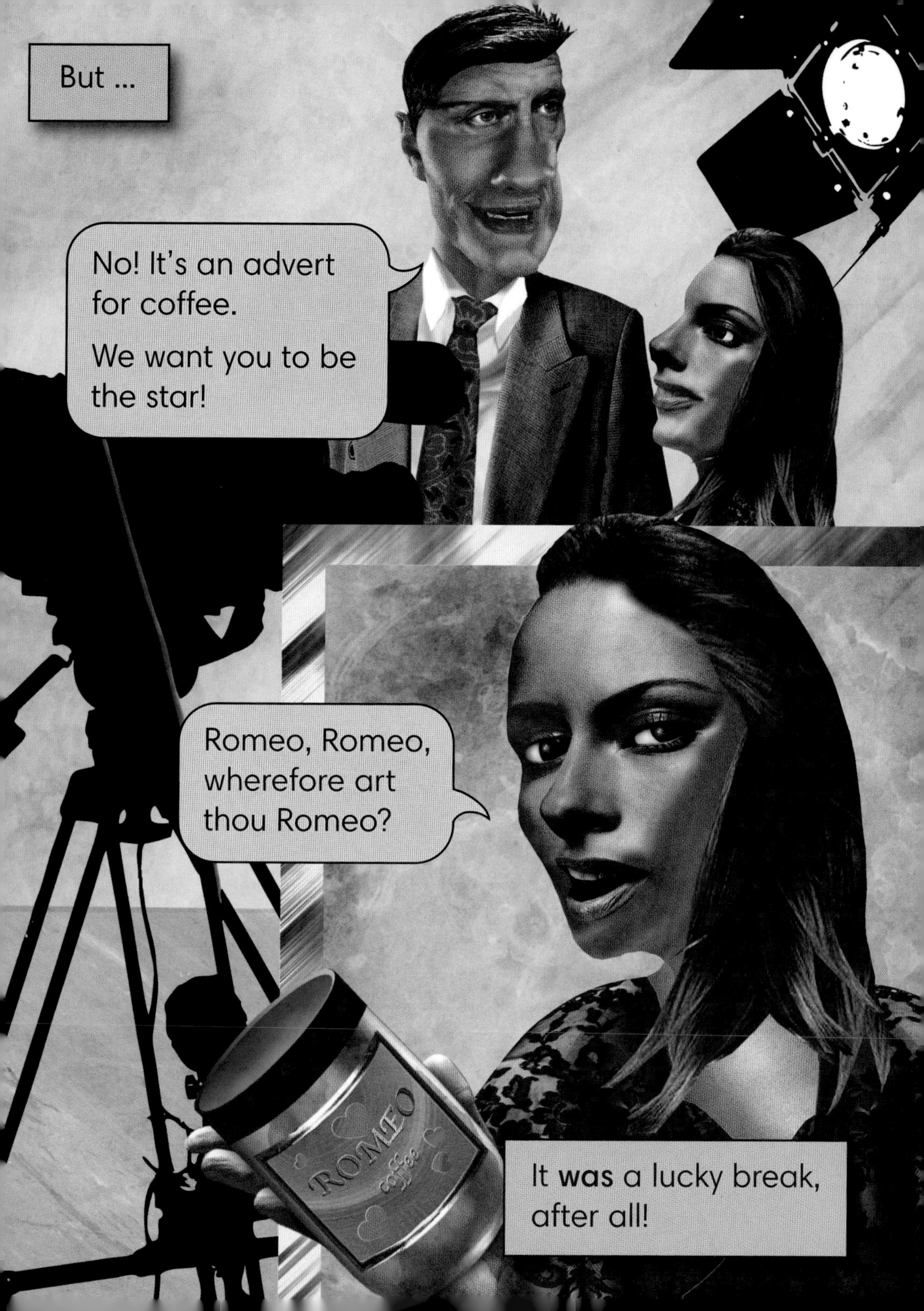

Curtain Call

agent	performance
audience	realistic
audition	scene
character	scenery
'in character'	script
director	stage
edit	stage lighting
experience	stage makeup
film	studio
lines	'take'
method acting	talent
'the method'	television
perform	theatre